Jackie
Bennett

Jackie
Bennett

Santa's Reindeer Story

To: JackieBennett

From: SantaClaus

Date: 11-13-2020

Jackie
Bennett

Text Copyright © 2016 by Brody Wheeler
Photography Copyright © 2016 Brody Wheeler
Brody Wheeler Photography
Attica, New York • USA
BrodyWheeler.com

"A Visit from St. Nicholas"
Authored by Clement Clarke Moore

Reindeer Handler & Story Inspiration by
Michael Jablonski Antler Ridge Farms
Hamburg, New York • USA
mikejab1@verizon.net

Published & Distributed by
Reindeer Promotions
4211 Rt 21 South
Canandaigua, New York • USA
reindeerpromotions.com
For more information (585) 340-7969.

Design & Page Layout by
Olive & Ink, LLC
Perry, New York • USA
oliveandink.com

Visit Santa's Reindeer Store at
santasreindeerstory.com

© Copyright Reindeer Promotions 2016

Signature Book Printing
www.sbpbooks.com

ISBN: 978-0-578-18525-5

Jackie
Bennett

Clement Clarke Moore's famous poem, which he named "A Visit From St. Nicholas," was published for the first time on December 23, 1823, by a Troy New York newspaper called the Sentinel. Since then, the poem has been reprinted, translated into almost every language known to man, and circulated throughout the world.

Clement's colorful and vivid description of the "chubby and plump, jolly old elf" redefined the world's timeless description of who we now know as Santa Claus. Before this poem was written, the world had not yet settled on a definitive look or characteristic of what Santa Claus should look like. The world-wide popularity of the poem solidified Santa Claus as the iconic figure we all now recognize as the red suited, white bearded, jolly old St. Nick.

The poem also introduces Santa's famous team of flying reindeer. In this book, I want to share with you the origins of each reindeers' name. Santa recognized the unique quality of each reindeer that pulls his sleigh with a special name. Some of those qualities the reindeer were born with, and some they developed over time. My hope is that you and your children receive years of enjoyment from this book and that young readers will identify with the positive attributes of these reindeer and be inspired to be the best that they can be.

Enjoy the book and have a Merry Christmas!

'Twas the night before Christmas, when all through the house
not a creature was stirring, not even a mouse.
The stockings were hung by the chimney with care,
in hopes that St. Nicholas soon would be there.

The children were nestled all snug in their beds,
while visions of sugar plums danced in their heads.
And Mama in her 'kerchief, and I in my cap,
had just settled our brains for a long winter's nap.

When out on the roof there arose such a clatter,
I sprang from my bed to see what was the matter.
Away to the window I flew like a flash,
tore open the shutter, and threw up the sash.

The moon on the breast of the new-fallen snow
gave the lustre of midday to objects below,
when, what to my wondering eyes should appear,
but a miniature sleigh and eight tiny reindeer.

With a little old driver, so lively and quick,
I knew in a moment it must be St. Nick.
More rapid than eagles, his coursers they came,
and he whistled and shouted and called them by name:

"Now Dasher! Now Dancer!
Now, Prancer and Vixen!
On, Comet! On, Cupid!
On, Donner and Blitzen!
To the top of the porch!
To the top of the wall!
Now dash away! Dash away!
Dash away all!"

As dry leaves that before the wild hurricane fly,
when they meet with an obstacle, mount to the sky
so up to the house-top the coursers they flew,
with the sleigh full of toys, and St. Nicholas too.

And then, in a twinkling, I heard on the roof
the prancing and pawing of each little hoof.
As I drew in my head and was turning around,
down the chimney St. Nicholas came with a bound.

He was dressed all in fur, from his head to his foot,
and his clothes were all tarnished with ashes and soot.
A bundle of toys he had flung on his back,
and he looked like a peddler just opening his pack.

His eyes--how they twinkled! His dimples, how merry!
His cheeks were like roses, his nose like a cherry!
His droll little mouth was drawn up like a bow,
and the beard on his chin was as white as the snow.
The stump of a pipe he held tight in his teeth,
and the smoke it encircled his head like a wreath.
He had a broad face and a little round belly,
that shook when he laughed, like a bowl full of jelly.

He was chubby and plump, a right jolly old elf,
and I laughed when I saw him, in spite of myself.
A wink of his eye and a twist of his head
soon gave me to know I had nothing to dread.

He spoke not a word, but went straight to his work,
and filled all the stockings, then turned with a jerk.
And laying his finger aside of his nose,
and giving a nod, up the chimney he rose.

He sprang to his sleigh, to his team gave a whistle,
And away they all flew like the down of a thistle.
But I heard him exclaim, 'ere he drove out of sight,
"Happy Christmas to all, and to all a good night!"

Dasher

When Dasher was born, Santa noticed almost
immediately that he was a natural leader.
As a young buck he displayed a self-confidence
that was unusual for such a young deer. He soon grew
to be a very determined and brave leader in Santa's herd.
Santa felt that the name Dasher suited him perfectly.

Dasher & Santa

Dancer & Santa

Dancer

Dancer was the young deer that would
always make the other reindeer laugh.
All of the other reindeer loved him for his
adventurous spirit and boundless energy.
The day he was born, as he learned to walk,
with his little legs wobbling back and forth,
Santa thought he looked like he was dancing.
Chuckling to himself, Santa thought
"I will name him Dancer."

Prancer

Prancer was born during a very harsh winter.
The North Pole saw record snow fall that year.
Santa watched as a very young reindeer was trying
to run through the deep snow. The reindeer was lifting
his legs as high as he could moving through the snow with
very high springing steps. Santa knew right away that
he would name him Prancer. Prancer soon became one
of Santa's most reliable and well-mannered reindeer.
Prancer's self-control and trustworthy character
made him a favorite among all of the other reindeer.

Prancer & Santa

Vixen & Santa

Vixen

As a young reindeer, Vixen was one of Santa's most beloved.
She was known for her sometimes shy and quiet demeanor.
Santa soon learned that having a really smart,
hardworking reindeer on the team would be very valuable.
Vixen's thoughtfulness and patience made her a
favorite among the other reindeer. Santa named her Vixen,
because her best friend growing up at the North Pole
was a young female fox, also known as a vixen.

Comet

Before this little guy received his name,
Santa and the other reindeer noticed how much
faster he was than every other reindeer his age.
Not only was he fast, he was also very bold and
courageous when he played with his friends.
Santa remembered that on the night he was born,
Haley's Comet was visible in the night sky.
Santa knew then that he had to name him Comet.

Comet & Santa

Cupid & Santa

Cupid

Santa has always had a soft spot for the curious
and carefree. These are just a couple of the qualities
that Santa observed in this young reindeer. Santa loved
how affectionate and gentle he was with all of the elves.
All the other reindeer loved his big heart,
so Santa decided to name him Cupid.

Donner

Santa is always on the look out for reindeer
who love a challenge and will finish any task he
or she sets out to accomplish. So, when Santa
witnessed the toughness and devotion demonstrated
by this reindeer, he knew he wanted him on his team.
His friends nicknamed him Thunder because of his
strength and speed. Santa liked the name as well, so he
named him Donner, the German word for thunder.

Donner & Santa

Blitzen & Santa

Blitzen

Growing up in the North Pole, this reindeer
was best friends with Donner. They were the same age
and they did everything together. They even had many of
the same qualities. Santa was impressed by his creativity.
Especially, when it came to solving some of Santa's biggest
problems. This, combined with his warm-hearted approach
to making friends, and his incredible speed, earned him the
nickname Lightning. Santa agreed, so he called him
Blitzen, the German word for lightning.

Rudolph

As many of you might already know, Rudolph was born much later than the rest of Santa's team of flying reindeer. In fact, Rudolph is the first born son of Donner. Rudolph was not like all of the other reindeer. He was born with a unique ability to make his nose glow bright red. One year, a terrible blizzard threatened to prevent Santa from delivering his toys on Christmas Eve. The wind and snow was so bad that Santa and his reindeer could not see to fly safely out of the North Pole. Santa remembered he had a young selfless reindeer who loved Christmas very much and would do anything he could to help Santa deliver his toys. Even though Rudolph was very young, Santa asked him if he would be willing to join the team using his bright red nose to lead the way through the heavy wind and snow that fateful Christmas Eve. Rudolph accepted the challenge and with tremendous strength and courage Rudolph helped Santa deliver all of the toys on time.

Rudolph & Santa

Name Our New Baby Boy Reindeer

This is one of our newest baby reindeer. He is very lovable and
determined. He is very young and needs a name.

Log on to santasreindeerstory.com

for your chance to name our new baby reindeer.

The reindeer is a very misunderstood animal. Many people do not believe reindeer exist and those that are shown are really deer with antlers "glued" on. This is not true, and reindeer really do exist; however, they are not native to the United States. All reindeer in the United States are domestic animals and do not run wild. They are native to northern Europe and Asia. Their native region is called Lapland, which includes northern Norway, Finland, Sweden, and Siberia in Russia.

Unlike the deer native to North America, both male and female reindeer grow antlers. These antlers are shed each year in late winter or early spring. The female reindeer typically keep their antlers longer than the males.

The size of a reindeer's antlers is dependent on their age, diet, overall health, and genetics. The male reindeer tend to grow larger antlers than the females.

In their native region, the reindeer eat a combination of willow leaves, moss, and lichen.

When pregnant, the females typically carry only one calf. Born in early spring, the calves have dark fur, long legs, and weigh between 10 and 15 pounds.

By fall the new calves will weigh between 100 and 150 pounds and will stand approximately 3½ to 4 foot at the shoulder. When the calves are about a year old, they develop a tendon in the back of their ankle which rubs against the bone to cause a "clicking" noise. This enables them to follow the herd through blinding snow storms. The younger calves do not have this as they want to stay "invisible" to predators, but they are able to follow the clicking of the other reindeer to stay with the herd.

As you might imagine, reindeer love the cold weather. During the winter you can find them playing in the snow. They especially love the snowfall and can be found frolicking outside prior to it snowing. Sometimes reindeer can be a better weather indicator than the weatherman. Reindeer are very adaptable to many different environments. Their winter fur consists of hollow hairs which trap air and helps to insulate them from the cold. When it gets below freezing, reindeer have the unique ability to slow down the blood flow to their legs to reduce heat loss. In the summer, they restrict their activity during the hottest hours of the day and begin to frolic and play around dusk and through the night. During the day, they like to find cool dark places to lie around in. They also enjoy playing in the rain.

Reindeer are very unique and friendly animals. They are easy to train, almost like a dog. They are very smart animals and are not easy to fool. That is why they are used to pull sleighs and as pack animals in their native regions.

Dear Children,

I hope that you enjoyed learning more about the wonderful reindeer that pull my sleigh. Just as each of my reindeer are important and unique, so are you. I hope that you could see some of the same characteristics that make you special in one or more of my reindeer. Maybe you are strong and brave like Donner or thoughtful and kind like Cupid. These remarkable reindeer stood out from the crowd with their positive personal qualities and became leaders among the herd. You too can live a life that will set you apart from the crowd. Love, joy, peace, patience, kindness, goodness, faithfulness, gentleness, and self-control are some of the qualities we should all strive to live out every day. Find ways to show love to your family and friends this coming year, and you too can be as special as all my reindeer.

Santa

Santa's Reindeer Story LLC is proud to announce
a portion of the proceeds from this book will go
to benefit reindeer research all across the country.

Go to santasreindeerstory.com to find out more
information on how you can help the reindeer.

Thank you Clement Clarke Moore for creating what many consider to be some of the most famous words even written by an American poet. This book was certainly inspired by your iconic poem "A visit from St. Nicholas" written almost 200 years ago.

Jackie Bennett

Jackie
Bennett

Jackie
Bennett